A TREASURY
OF
BEST LOVED RHYMES

ILLUSTRATED BY
CHARLES ROBINSON

This edition is distributed by
AVENEL BOOKS
a division of Crown Publishers, Inc.

Contents

A MEDLEY

O N Christmas Eve I turned the spit,
I burnt my fingers, I feel it yet;
The cock sparrow flew over the table,
The pot began to play with the ladle;
The ladle stood up like a naked man,
And vowed he 'd fight the frying-pan;
The frying-pan behind the door
Said he never saw the like before;
And the kitchen clock I was going to wind
And he never saw the like behind.

THE WISE MEN OF GOTHAM

Three wise men of Gotham
They went to sea in a bowl;
And if the bowl had been stronger,
My song had been longer.

THE QUEEN of HEARTS

The Queen of Hearts she
made some tarts,

All on a summer's day;

The Knave of Hearts he stole those
tarts,

And took them clean away.

The King of Hearts
called for those
tarts,

nd beat the
Knave full
sore.

The Queen of Hearts

The Knave of Hearts

        brought back those tarts,

And vowed he 'd steal no more.

TO MARKET

To market, to market,
  To buy a fat pig;
Home again, home again,
  Jiggety jig.

To market, to market,
  To buy a fat hog;
Home again, home again,
  Jiggety jog.

Cock-a-doodle--do

COCK-A-DOODLE-DO

Cock-a-doodle-do!
My dame has lost her shoe;
My master's lost his fiddle-stick,
And don't know what to do.

Cock-a-doodle-do!
What is my dame to do?
Till master finds his fiddle-stick,
She'll dance without her shoe.

Tom, Tom, the Piper's Son

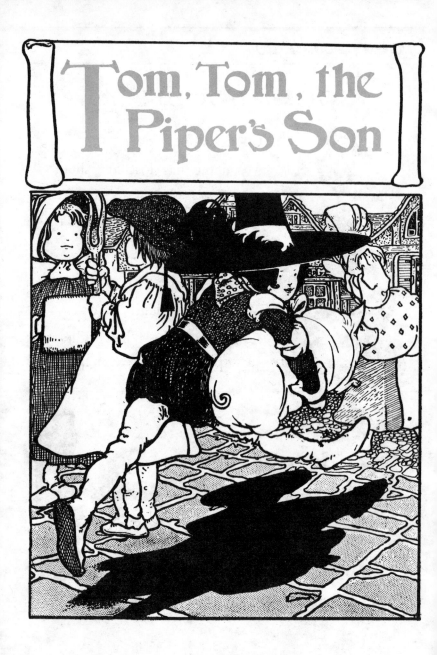

TOM, THE PIPER'S SON

Tom, Tom, the piper's son,
Stole a pig and away he run!
The pig was eat and Tom was beat,
And Tom went howling down the street.

THE WIND

When the wind is in the East,
'T is neither good for man nor beast;
When the wind is in the North,
The skilful fisher goes not forth;
When the wind is in the South,
It blows the bait in the fish's mouth;
When the wind is in the West,
Then 't is at the very best.

HUMPTY-DUMPTY

HUMPTY-DUMPTY sat on a wall,
Humpty-Dumpty had a great fall;

Threescore men, and threescore more,
Cannot place Humpty-Dumpty as he
was before.

WHAT ARE LITTLE BOYS MADE OF?

What are little boys made of, made of?
What are little boys made of?
Snips and snails, and puppy-dogs' tails;
That's what little boys are made
of, made of.

What are little girls made of,
made of?
What are little girls made of?
Sugar and spice, and all things nice,
That's what little girls are made
of, made of.

15

A FROG HE WOULD A·WOOING GO.

A frog he would a-wooing go,
      Heigho! says Rowley,
Whether his mother would let him or no.
    With a rowley powley, gammon and spinach,
    Heigho! says Anthony Rowley.

So off he set with his
  opera hat,
Heigho! says Rowley,
And on the road he
  met with a rat.
With a rowley powley,
  gammon and spinach,
Heigho! says Anthony
  Rowley.

"Pray, Mr. Rat, will
  you go with me?"
Heigho! says Rowley,
"Kind Mistress Mous-
  ey for to see!"
With a rowley powley,
  gammon and spinach,
Heigho! says Anthony
  Rowley.

When they reached the
  door of Mousey's hall,
Heigho! says Rowley,
They gave a loud knock,
  and they gave a loud
  call.
With a rowley powley,
  gammon and spinach,
Heigho! says Anthony
  Rowley.

Pray, Mistress Mouse, are you within?"

Heigho! says Rowley;
Oh, yes, kind sirs, I'm sitting to spin."

With a rowley powley,
gammon and spinach,
eigho! says Anthony Rowley.

Pray, Mistress Mouse, will you give us some beer?"

Heigho! says Rowley,
For Froggy and I are fond of good cheer."

With a rowley powley,
gammon and spinach,
eigho! says Anthony Rowley.

" Pray, Mr. Frog, will you give us a song?"

Heigho! says Rowley;
" But let it be something that's not very long."

With a rowley powley,
gammon and spinach,
Heigho! says Anthony Rowley.

" Indeed, Mistress Mouse," replied Mr. Frog,

Heigho! says Rowley,
" A cold has made me as hoarse as a hog."

With a rowley powley,
gammon and spinach,
Heigho! says Anthony Rowley.

" Since you have caught cold, Mr. Frog," Mousey said
    Heigho! says Rowley,
" I 'll sing you a song that I
    have just made."
    With a rowley powley,
        gammon and spinach,
Heigho! says Anthony Rowley.

But while they were all a merr
    making,
    Heigho! says Rowley,
A cat with her kittens ca
    tumbling in.
    With a rowley powley,
        gammon and spinac
Heigho! says Anthony Rowle

The cat she seized
    the rat by the crown,
    Heigho! says Rowley,
The kittens they pulled
    the little mouse down.
    With a rowley powley, gam-
        mon and spinach,
Heigho! says Anthony Rowley.

his put Mr. Frog in a
terrible fright,
　　Heigho! says Rowley;
He took up his hat and he
wished them good-night.
　　　With a rowley powley,
　　　　gammon and spinach,
Heigho! says Anthony Rowley.

But as Froggy was crossing
over a brook,
　　Heigho! says Rowley,
A lily-white duck came and
gobbled him up.
　　　With a rowley powley,
　　　　gammon and spinach,
Heigho! says Anthony Rowley.

So there was an end of one, two, and three,
　　　　Heigho! says Rowley,
The Rat, the Mouse, and the little Frog-gee!
　　　With a rowley powley, gammon and spinach,
　　　Heigho! says Anthony Rowley.

 HEN good King Arthur ruled this
land

He was a goodly king;

He stole three pecks of barley-meal

To make a bag-pudding.

bag-pudding the
    king did make,
And stuff'd it well
    with plums;

23

And in it put great lumps of fat,
    As big as my two thumbs.

The king and queen did eat thereof,
    And noble men beside;
And what they could not eat that night,
    The queen next morning fried.

SOLOMON GRUNDY

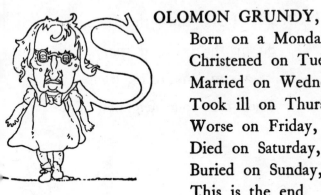

OLOMON GRUNDY,
Born on a Monday,
Christened on Tuesday,
Married on Wednesday,
Took ill on Thursday,
Worse on Friday,
Died on Saturday,
Buried on Sunday,
This is the end
Of Solomon Grundy.

THREE BLIND MICE

Three blind mice, three blind mice,
They all ran after the
    farmer's wife,
She cut off their tails with
    a carving knife;
Did you ever see such a
    thing in your life

As three blind mice?

CROSS-PATCH

CROSS-PATCH, draw the latch,
    Sit by the fire and spin;
Take a cup, and drink it up,
    Then call your neighbours in.

YANKEE DOODLE

Yankee Doodle came to town,
    Mounted on a pony;
He stuck a feather in his cap
    And called it Maccaroni.

Yankee Doodle came to town,
    Yankee Doodle dandy,
He stuck a feather in his cap
    And called it sugar-candy.

WINKLE, twinkle, little star,
How I wonder what you are!

Twinkle, twinkle, little Star

Up above the world so high,
Like a diamond in the sky.

When the blazing sun is gone,
When he nothing shines upon,
Then you show your little light,
Twinkle, twinkle, all the night.

Then the traveller in the dark
Thanks you for your tiny spark:
How could he see where to go,
If you did not twinkle so?

In the dark blue sky you keep,
Often through my curtains peep,
For you never shut your eye
Till the sun is in the sky.

How your bright and tiny spark
Lights the traveller in the dark!
Though I know not what you **are**,
Twinkle, twinkle, little star.

TOAD AND FROG

"Croak," said the toad, "I 'm hungry
    I think,
To-day I 've had nothing to eat or
    to drink;
I 'll crawl to a garden and jump
    through the pales,
And there I 'll dine nicely on slugs and on snails."

"Ho, ho!" quoth the frog, "is that what you mean?
Then I 'll hop away to the next meadow stream,
There I will drink, and eat worms and slugs too,
And then I shall have a good dinner like you."

LITTLE
JACK HORNER

Little Jack Horner
Sat in a corner
Eating of Christmas pie;

He put in his thumb,
And pulled out a plum,
And cried "What a good boy
    was I!"

THERE WAS A LITTLE MAN

THERE was a little man, and
he had a little gun,

And his bullets they were
made of lead, lead, lead.

He shot Johnny Sprig through
the middle of his wig,

And knocked it right
off his head, head,
head.

HEY! DIDDLE, DIDDLE

HEY! diddle, diddle,
The cat and the fiddle,
The cow jumped over the moon;
The little dog laughed
To see such craft,
And the dish ran away with the spoon.

TWO LITTLE BIRDS

There were two blackbirds
Sat upon a hill,
The one named Jack,
The other named Jill.
Fly away, Jack!
Fly away, Jill!
Come again, Jack!
Come again, Jill!

ING a song of sixpence,
  Pockets full of rye;
Four and twenty black-
    birds
  Baked in a pie.

When the pie was opened
  The birds began to
    sing;
Was not that a dainty dish
  To set before the king?

The king was in his counting-
house

Counting out his money;

The queen was in the parlour,

Eating bread and honey;

Sing a Song of Sixpence

The maid was in the garden
Hanging out the clothes,
Down came a blackbird,
And snapped off her nose.

The Old Woman who lived in a Shoe

THE OLD WOMAN WHO LIVED IN A SHOE

THERE was an old woman who lived in a shoe,

She had so many children she didn't know what to do;

She gave them some broth without any bread,

Then whipped them all round, and sent them to bed.

BUTTONS

BUTTONS, a farthing a pair,
  Come, who will buy them of me?
  They 're round and sound and pretty,
  And fit for the girls of the city.
  Come, who will buy them of me,
  Buttons, a farthing a pair?

SULKY SUE

Here 's Sulky Sue;
What shall we do?
Turn her face to the wall
Till she comes to.

A DILLER, A DOLLAR.

A diller, a dollar,
A ten o'clock scholar;
What makes you come so soon?
You used to come at ten o'clock,
But now you come at noon.

Three
Jolly Welshmen

Three Jolly Welshmen.

There were three jolly Welshmen,
    As I have heard say,
And they went a-hunting
    Upon St. David's day.

All the day they hunted,
    And nothing could they find;

But a ship a-sailing,
    A-sailing with the wind.

One said it was a ship,
    The other he said " Nay ";
The third he said it was a house,
    With the chimney blown away.

And all the night they hunted,
    And nothing could they find,
But the moon a-gliding,
    A-gliding with the wind.

One said it was the moon,
    The other he said " Nay ";
The third he said it was a cheese,
    With half o' it cut away.

THREE MEN IN A TUB

Rub-a-dub-dub,

Three men in a tub;

And who do you think they be?

The butcher, the baker,

The candlestick-maker;

Turn 'em out, knaves all three!

43

CURLY LOCKS

Thou shalt sit on a cushion and sew a fine seam, And feed upon strawberries sugar and cream.

CURLY LOCKS

Curly locks! curly locks!
  wilt thou be mine?
Thou shalt not wash dishes,
  nor yet feed the swine;
But sit on a cushion, and
  sew a fine seam,
And feed upon strawberries,
  sugar, and cream!

Little Bo-peep

Little Bo-Peep

Little Bo-Peep has lost her sheep,
    And can 't tell where to find them;
Let them alone, and they 'll come home,
    And bring their tails behind them.

Little Bo-Peep fell fast asleep,
    And dreamt she heard them bleating;
And when she awoke, she found it a joke,
    For still they were all fleeting.

Then up she took her little
    crook,

Determined for to find them;

She found them indeed, but it made her heart bleed,
  For they 'd left all their tails behind them.

It happened one day as Bo-Peep did stray
  Into a meadow hard by,
There she espied their tails side by side,
  All hung on a tree to dry.

She heaved a sigh, and wiped her eye,

    And went over hill and dale, oh;

And tried what she could, as a shepherdess should

    To tack to each sheep its tail, oh!

JACK *and* JILL

Jack and Jill
        went up the hill,
To fetch a
        pail of water.

Jack and Jill

Jack fell down, and
broke his crown,

And Jill
came tumbling
after.

Then up Jack got,
   and off did trot,
As fast as he
   could caper,

To old Dame Dob,
   who patched his nob,
With vinegar and
   brown paper.

WEE WILLIE WINKIE

WEE WILLIE WINKIE runs through the town,

Up stairs and down stairs, in his night gown,

Rapping at the window, crying through the lock:

"Are the children in their beds, for it's past eight o'clock."

BAA, BAA, BLACK SHEEP

Baa, baa, black sheep, have you any wool?

Yes, marry, have I, three bags full:

One for my master, one for my dame,

But none for the little boy who cries in the lane.

HE FARMER AND HIS DAUGHTER

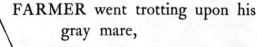

A FARMER went trotting upon his
gray mare,

    Bumpety, bumpety,
        bump!

With his daughter behind
him so rosy and fair,

    Lumpety, lumpety, lump!

raven cried "croak" and they all tumbled down,

    Bumpety, bumpety, bump!

he mare broke her knees, and the farmer his crown,

    Lumpety, lumpety, lump!

he mischievous raven flew laughing away,

    Bumpety, bumpety, bump!

nd vowed he would serve them the same the next day,

    Lumpety, lumpety, lump!

CHARLES ROBINSON

Simple Simon

SIMPLE SIMON

SIMPLE SIMON met a pie-man,
　　Going to the fair;
　Says Simple Simon to the pie-man,
　　" Let me taste your ware."

　Says the pie-man unto Simon,
　　" First give me a penny."
　Says Simple Simon to the pie-man,
　　" I have not got any."

He went to catch a dicky-bird,
　And thought he could not fail,
Because he had got a little salt
　To put upon his tail.

He went to
ride a
spotted cow,

That had got
a little
calf,

She threw him
down upon
the ground,

Which made
the people
laugh.

59

Simple Simon

Then Simple Simon went a-hunting,
    For to catch a hare,
He rode a goat about the street,
    But could not find one there.

He went for to eat honey
    Out of the mustard-pot,
He bit his tongue until he cried,
    That was all the good he got.

Simple Simon

SIMPLE SIMON went a-fishing
       For to catch a whale;
And all the water he had got
       Was in his mother's pail.

He went to take a bird's nest,
       Was built upon a bough;
A branch gave way, and Simon fell
       Into a dirty slough.

He went to shoot a
       wild duck,
But the wild duck
       flew away;
Says Simon, " I can't
       hit him,
Because he will not
       stay."

NCE Simon made a grea
Snowball,

And brought it in to roast

He laid it down before th
fire,

And soon the ball was los

E went to slide upon the ice,

Before the ice would bear;

Then he plunged in above his
knees,

Which made poor Simon stare.

He went to try if cherries ripe
Grew upon a thistle;
He pricked his finger very much,
Which made poor Simon whistle.

He washed himself with blacking-ball,
   Because he had no soap:
Then, then, said to his mother,
   "I'm a beauty now, I hope."

He went for water in a sieve,
   But soon it all ran through;
And now poor Simple Simon
   Bids you all adieu.